THIS BELONGS TO:

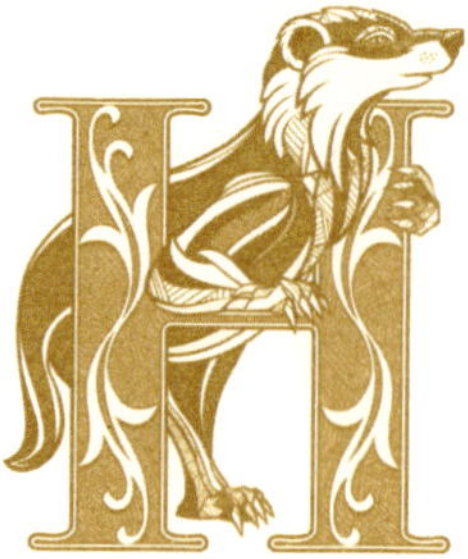

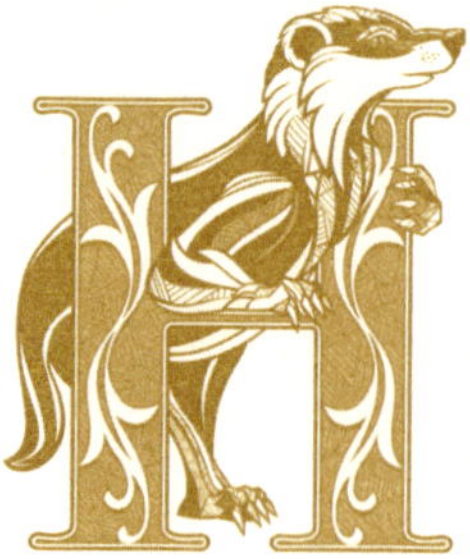

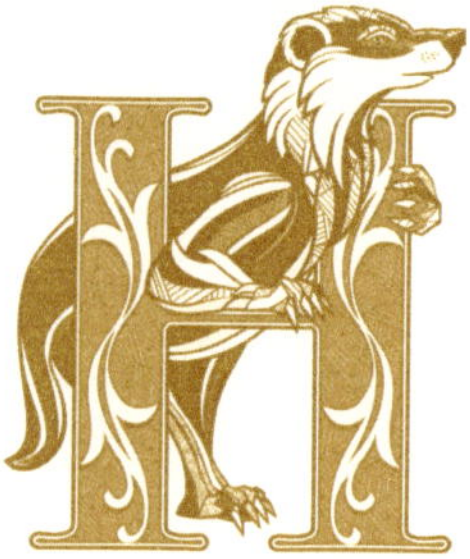

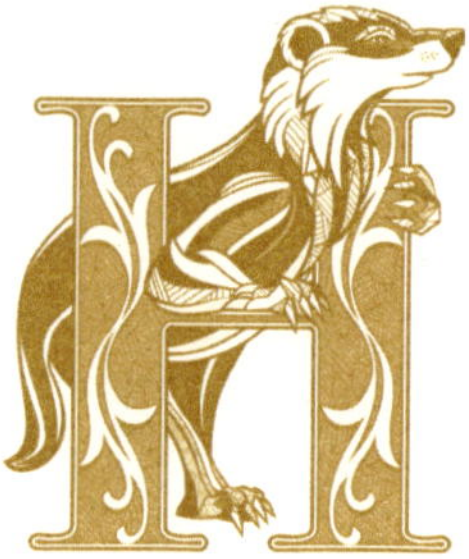

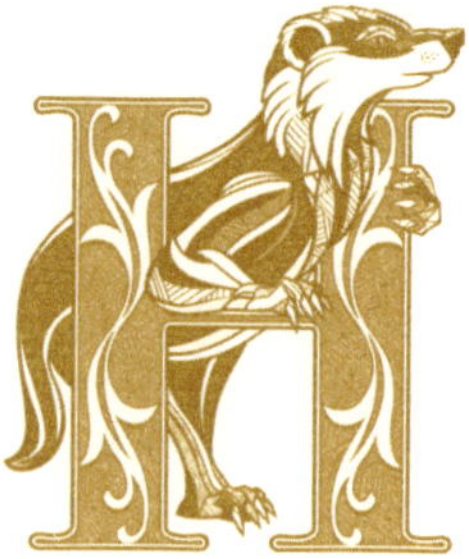

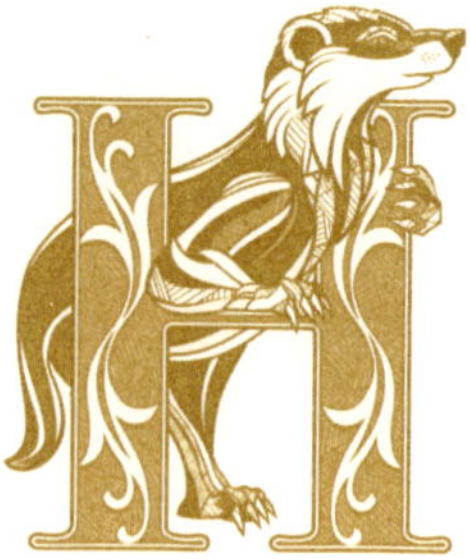

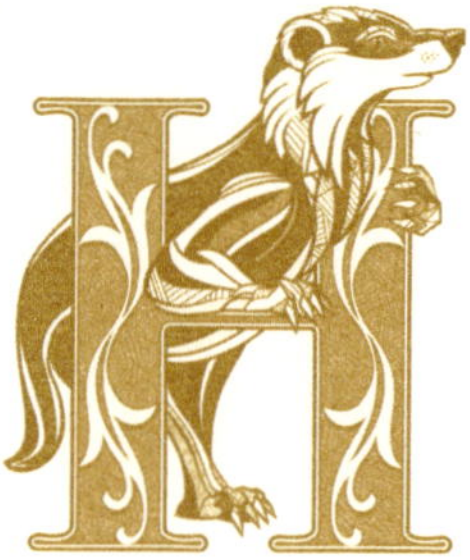

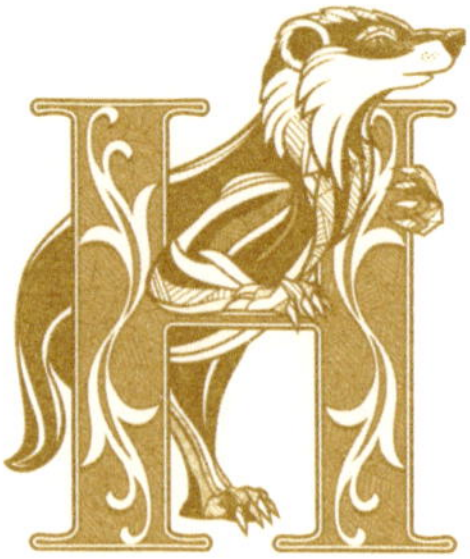

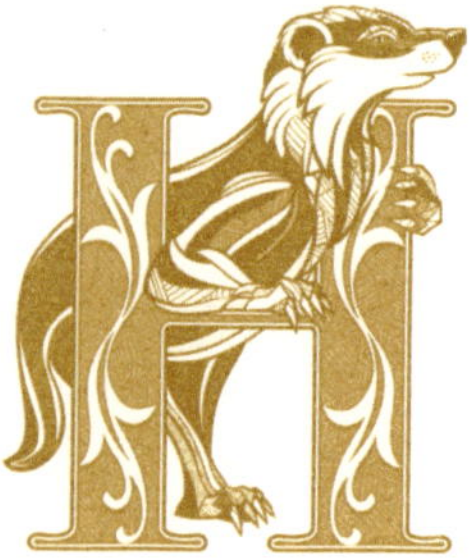

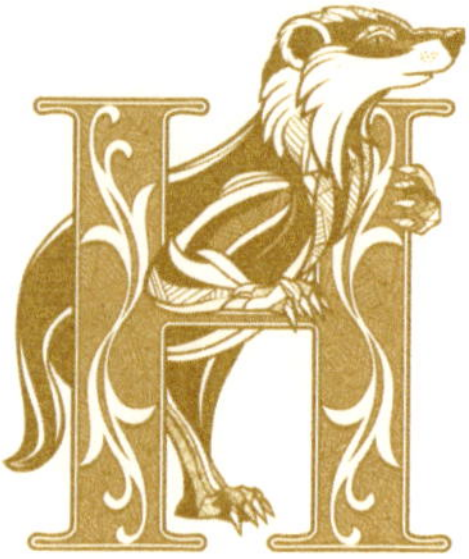

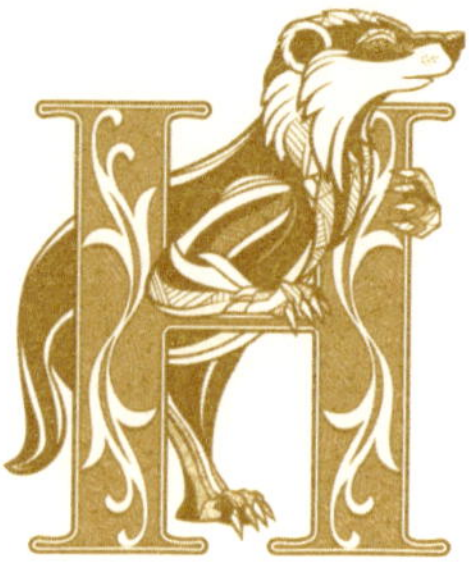

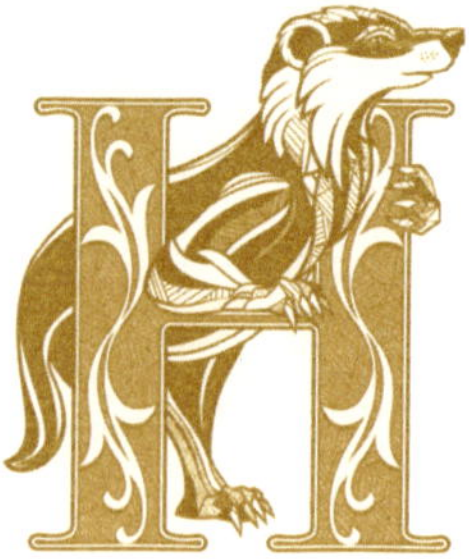

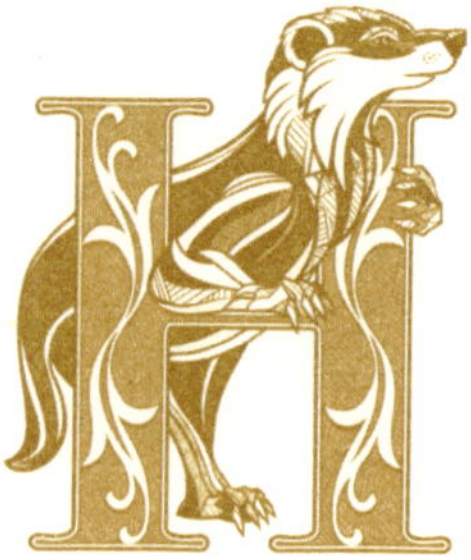

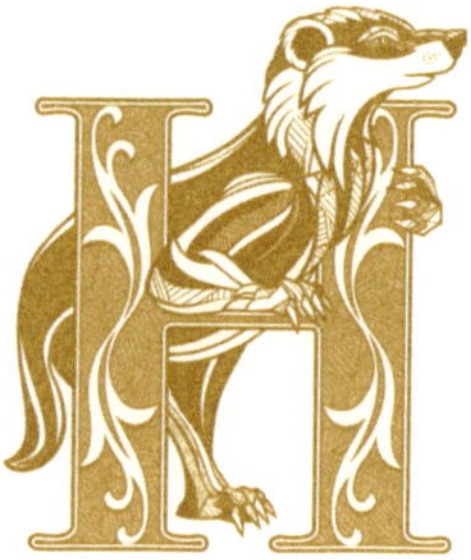

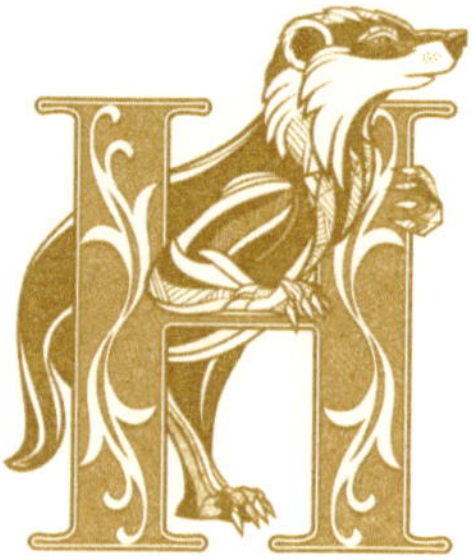

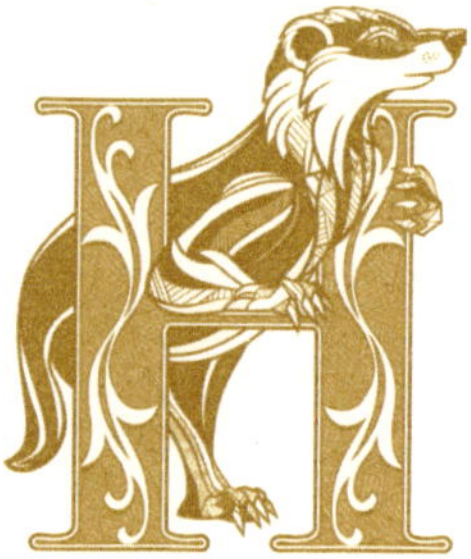

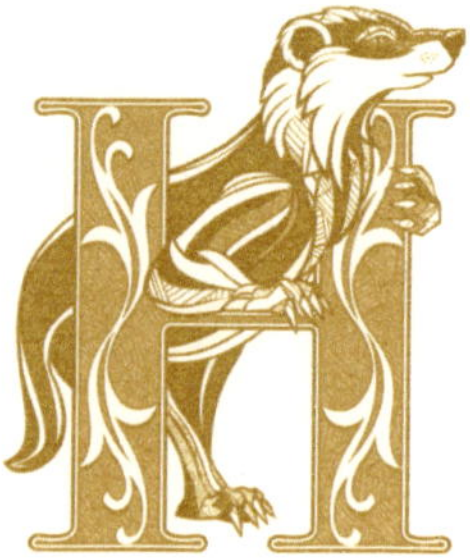

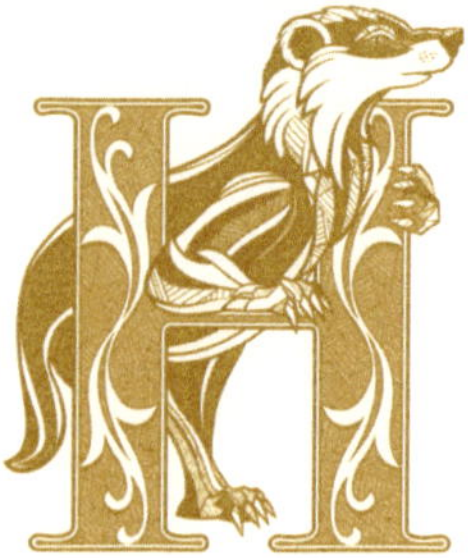

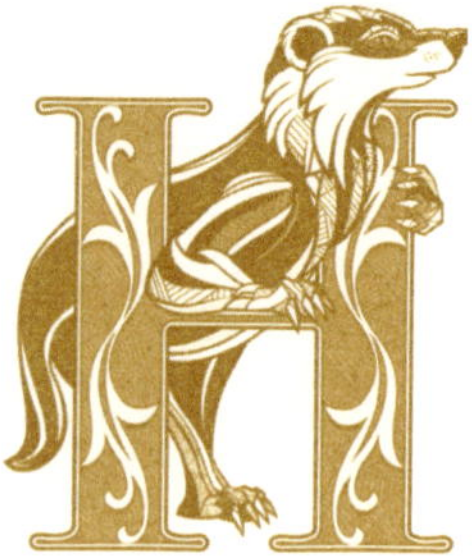

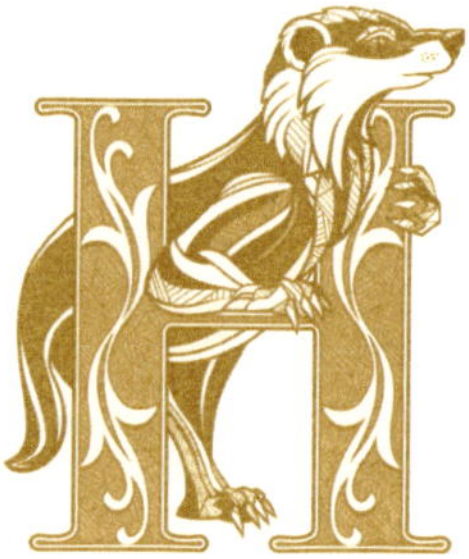

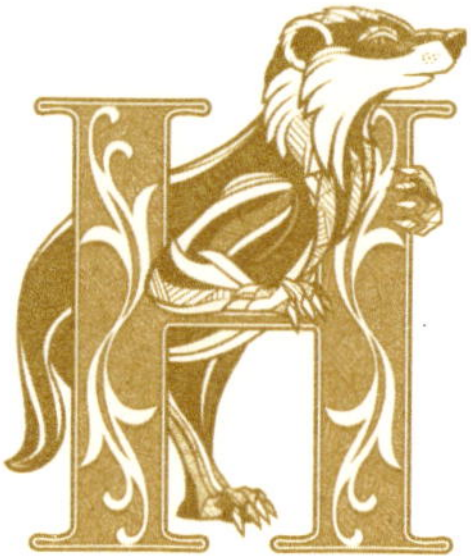

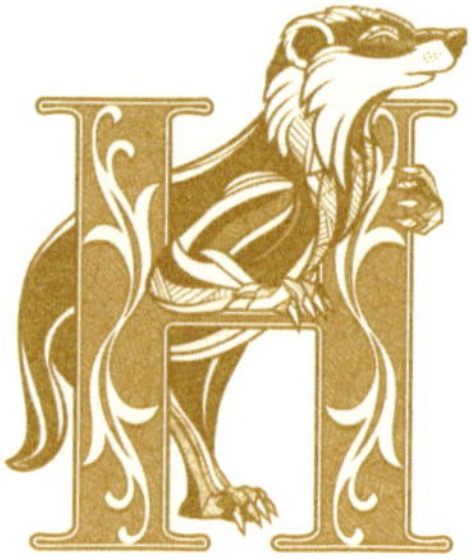

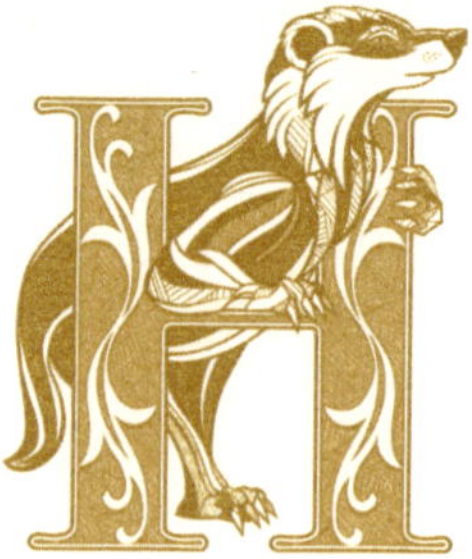

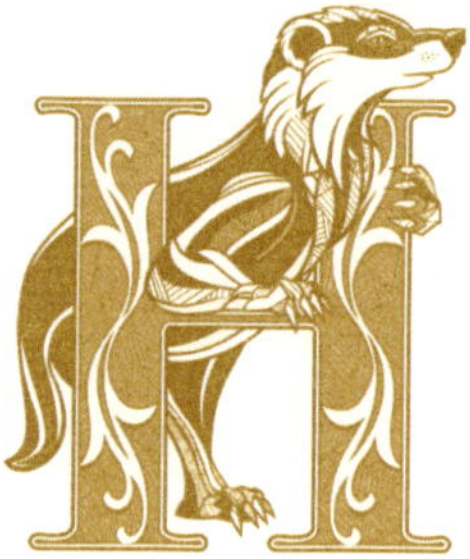

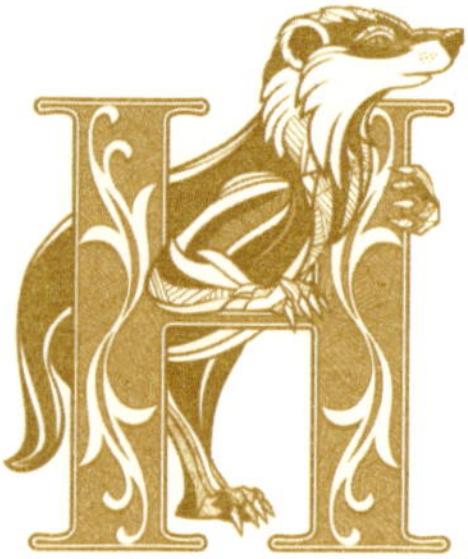

H

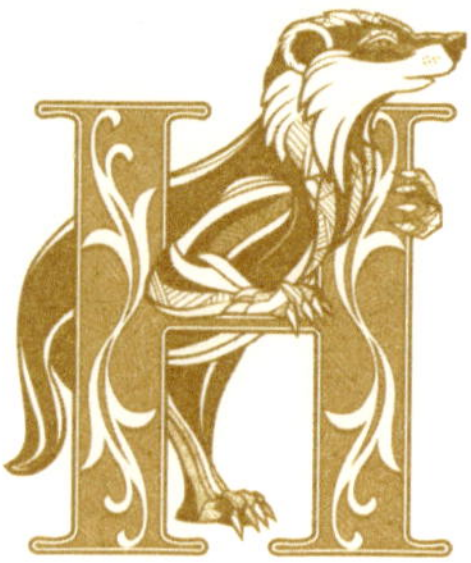

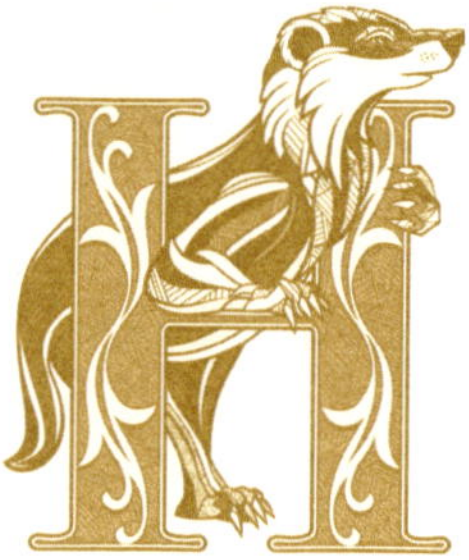

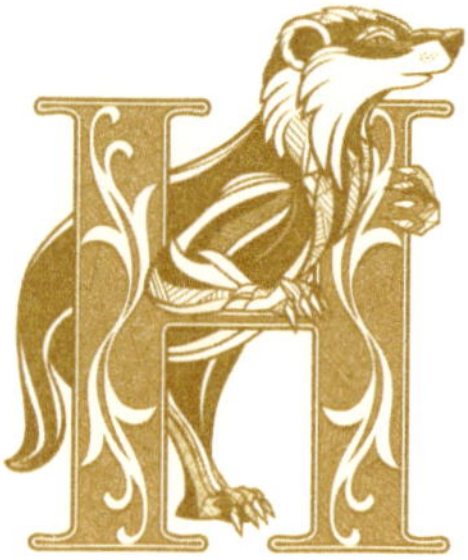

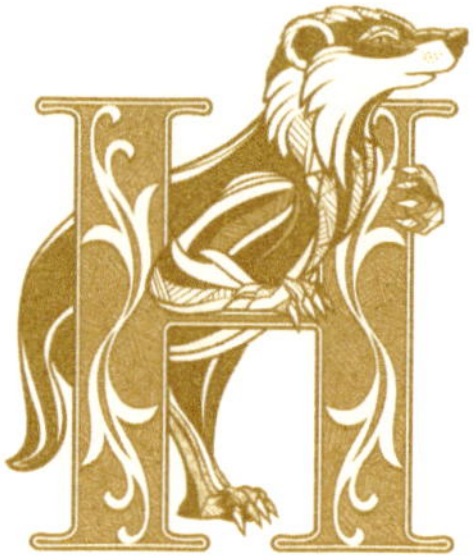

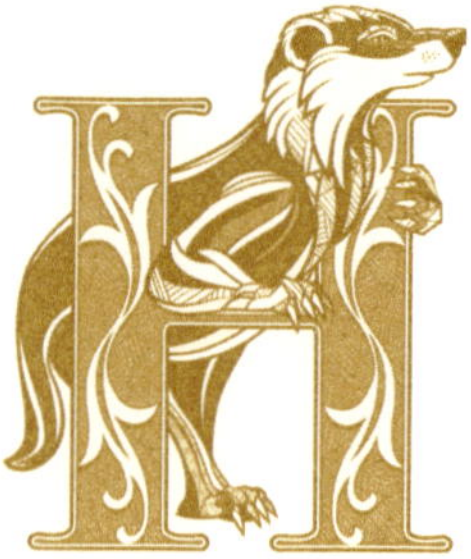

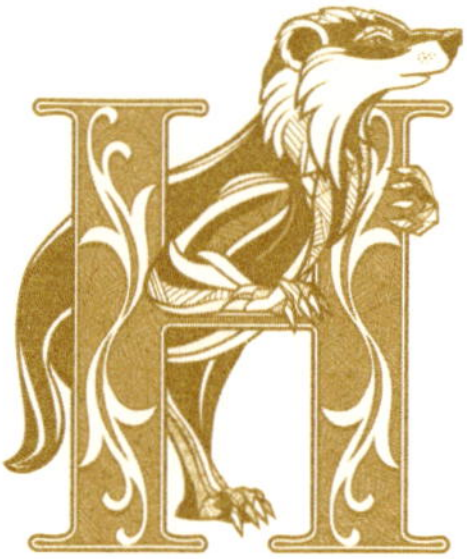

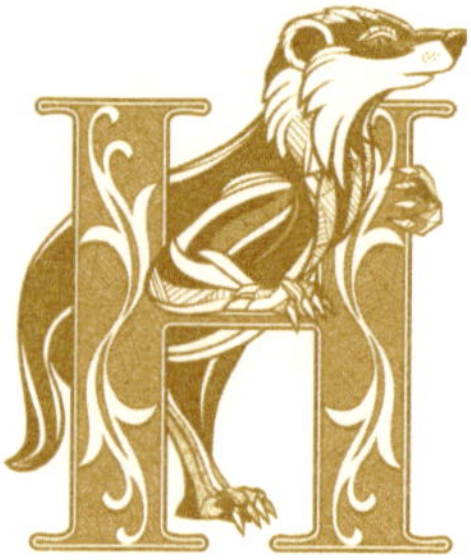

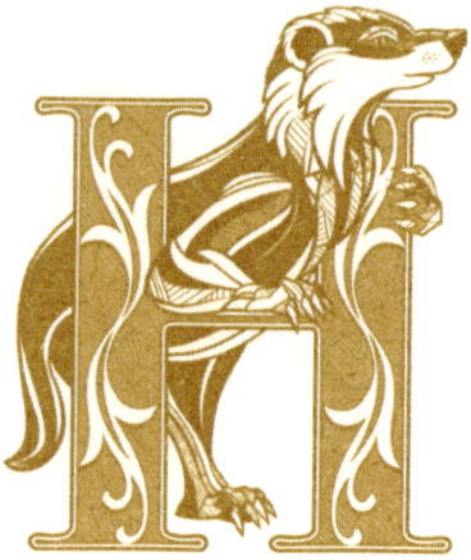

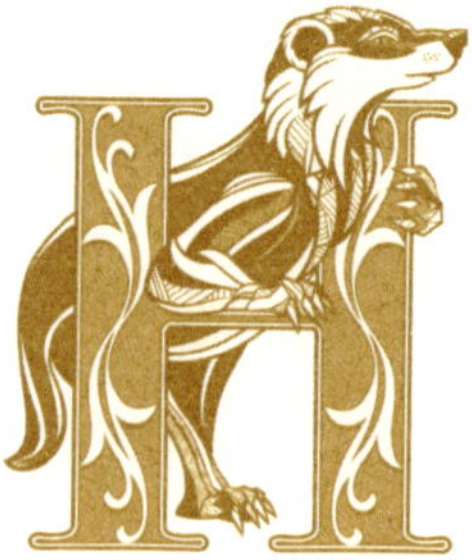

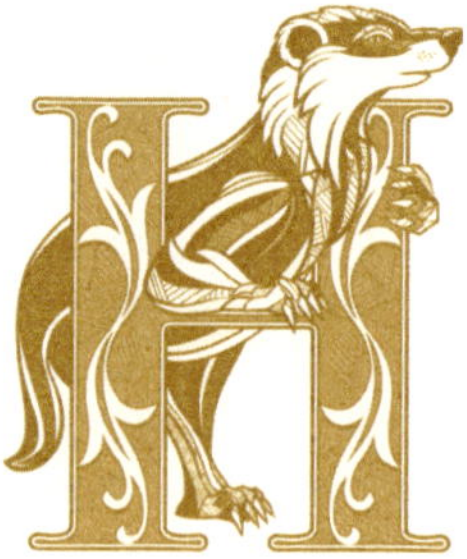

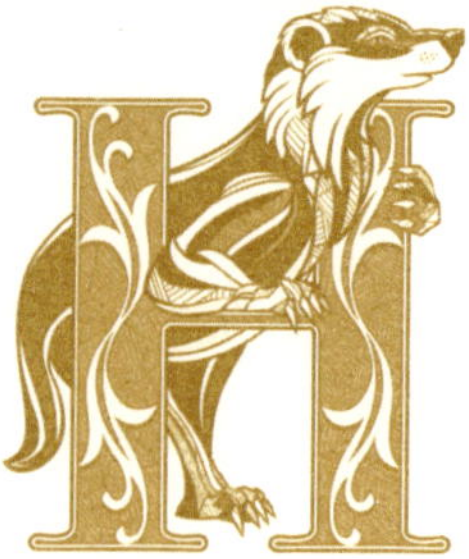

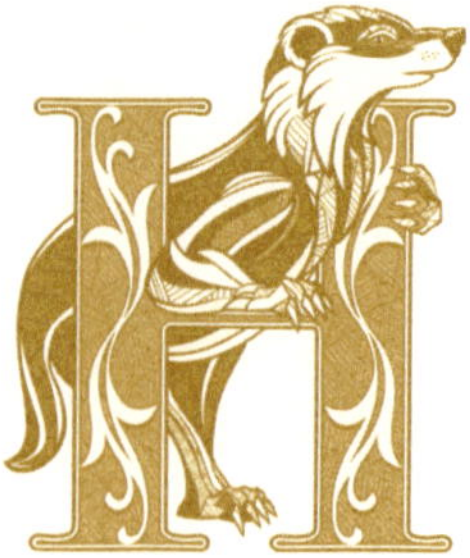

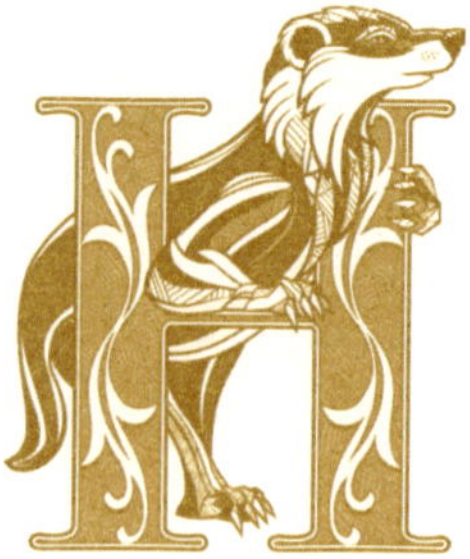

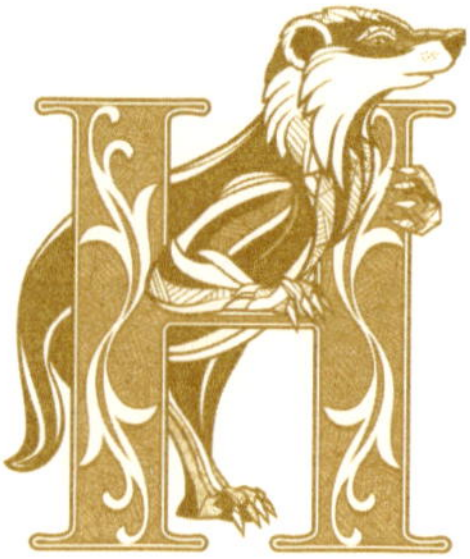

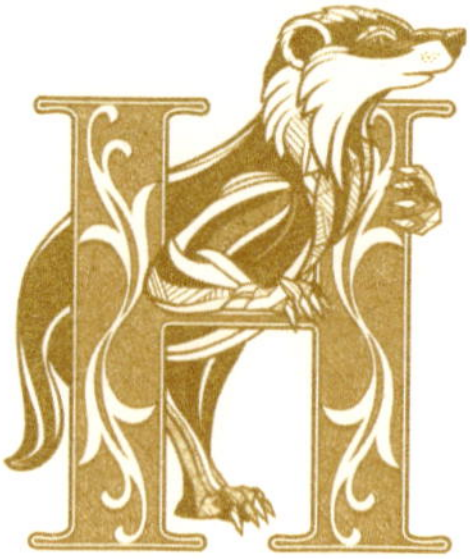

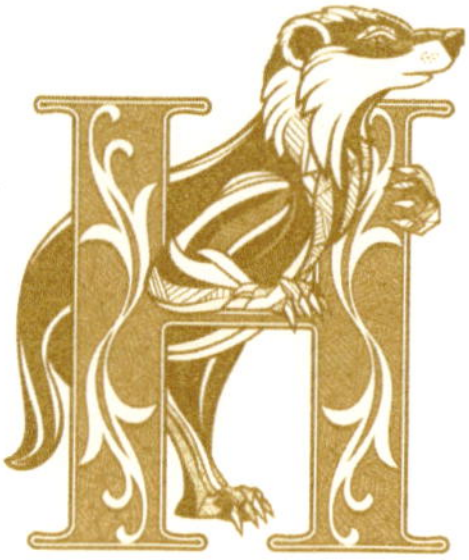

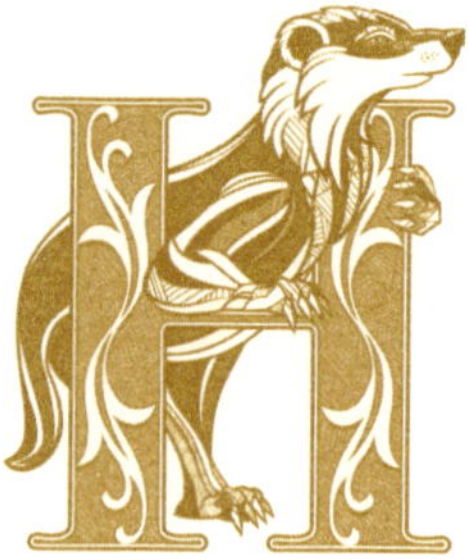

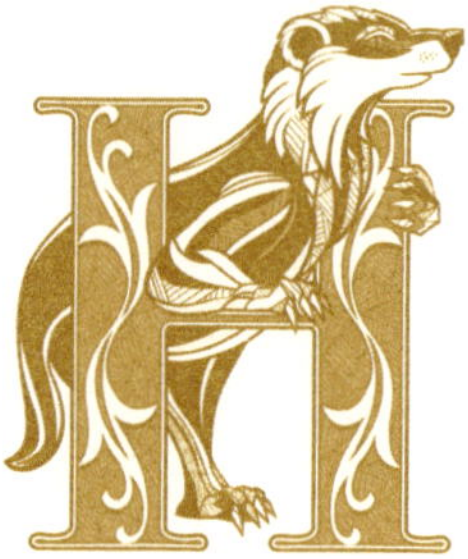

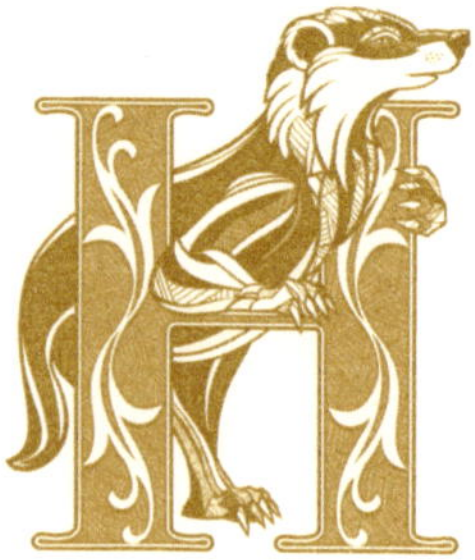

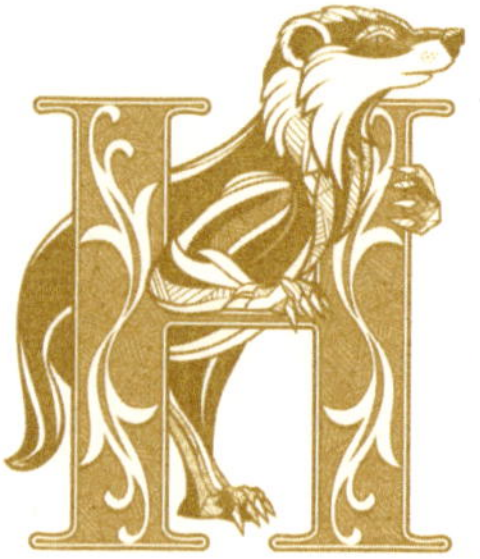

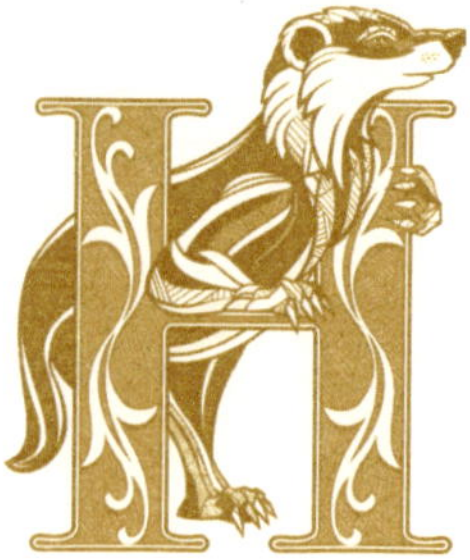

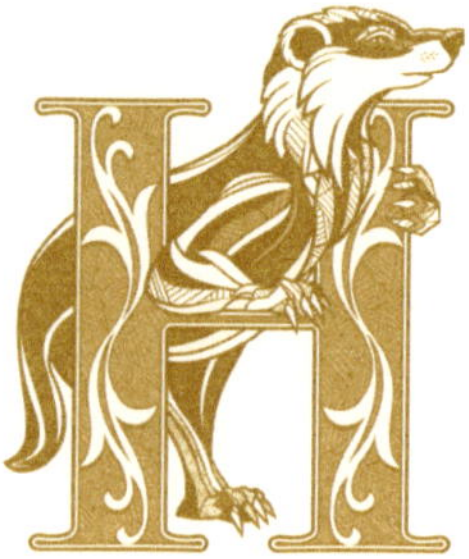

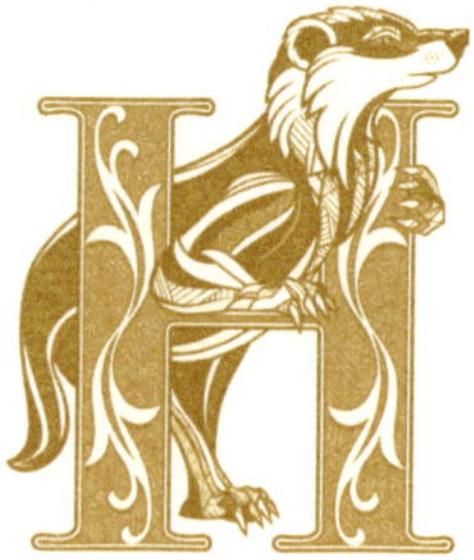

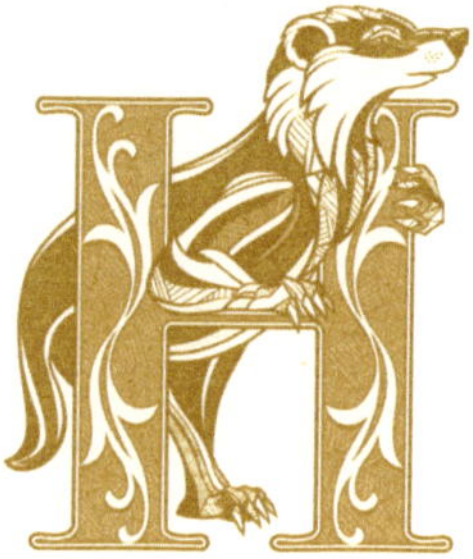

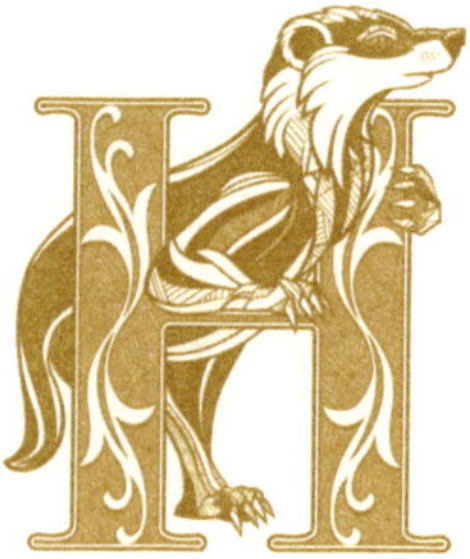

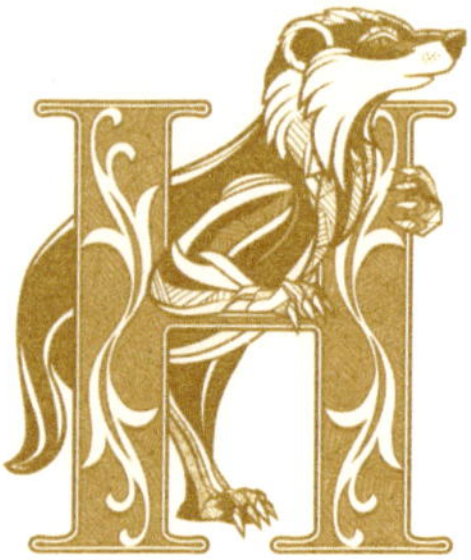

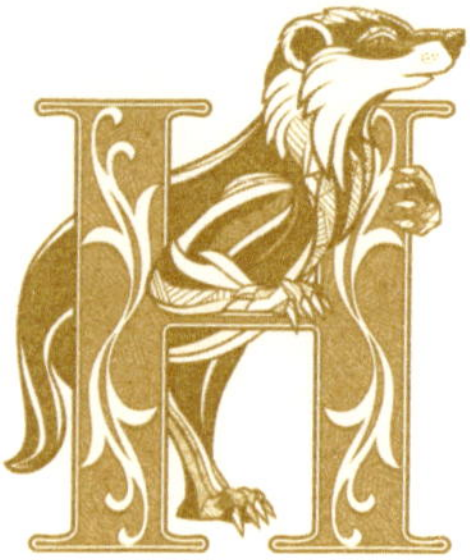

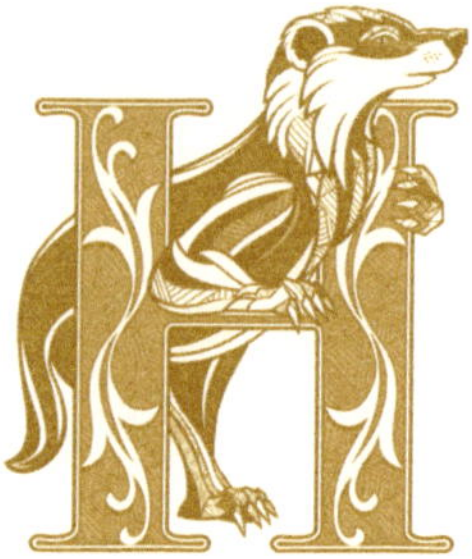

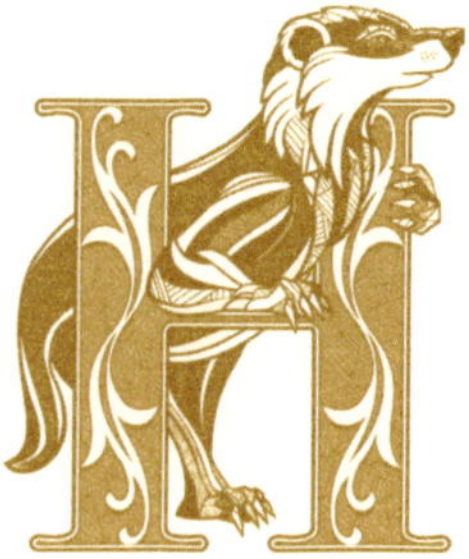

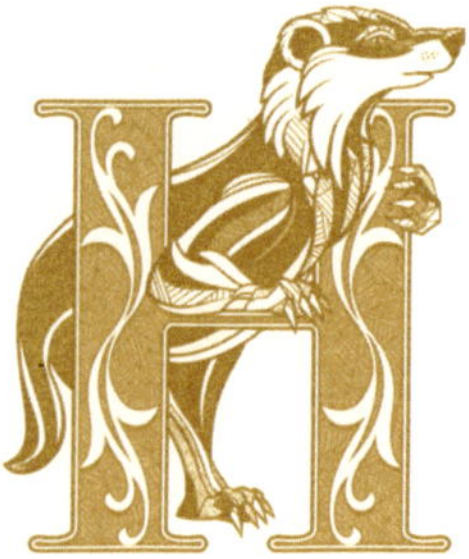

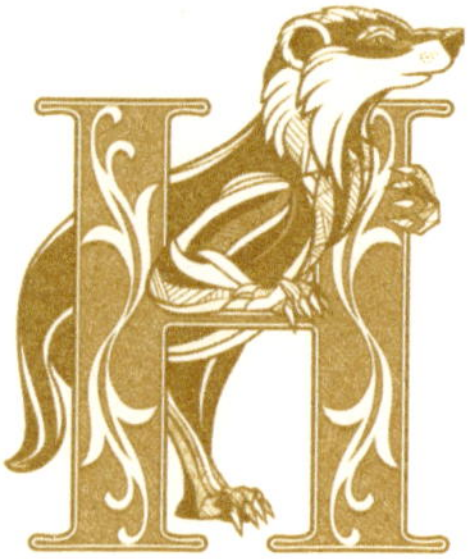

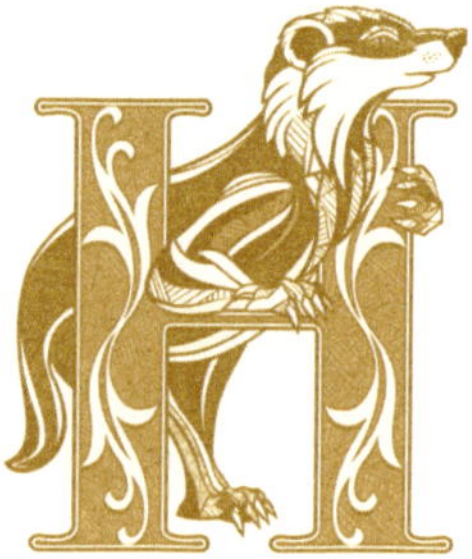

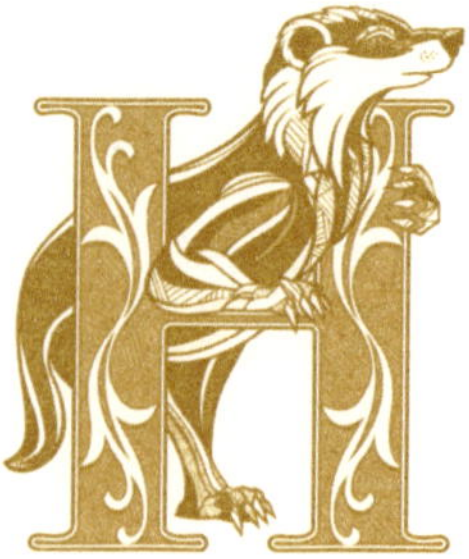

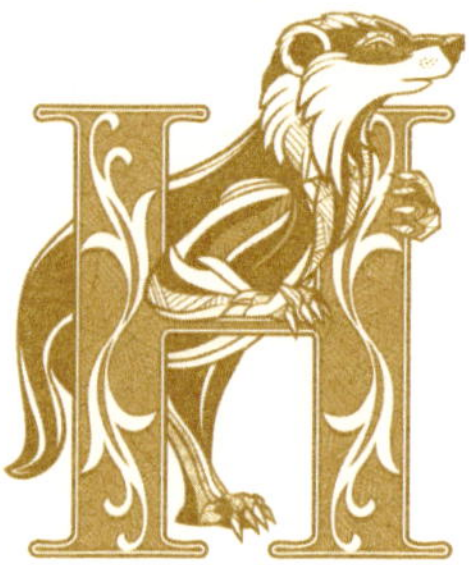

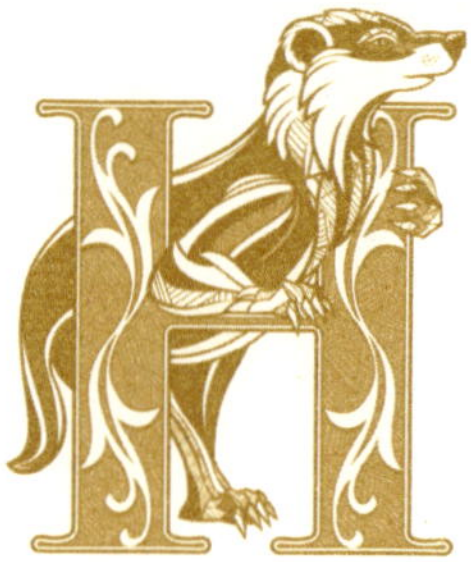

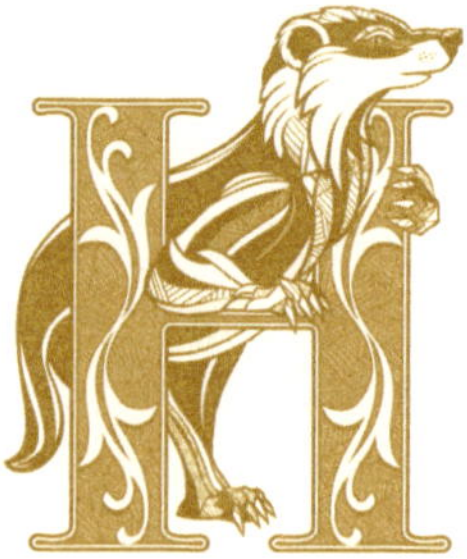

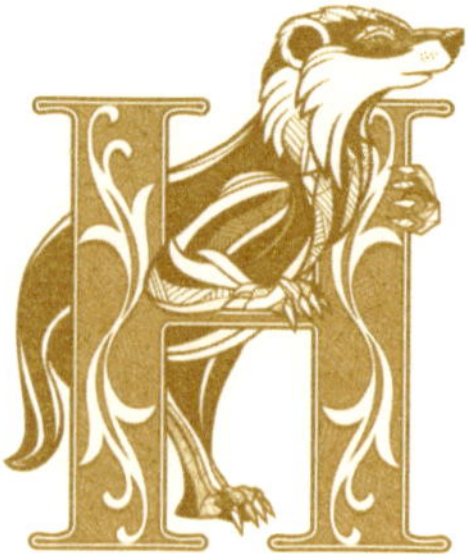

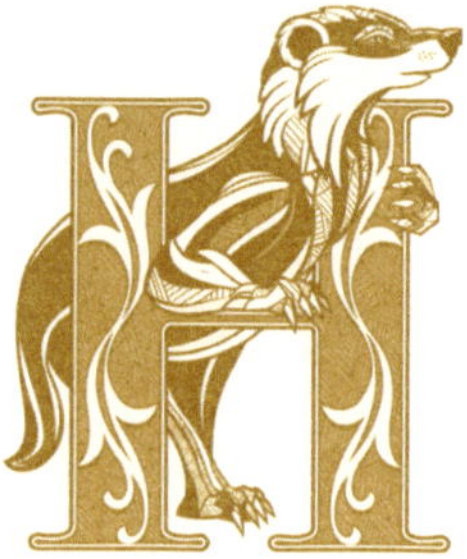

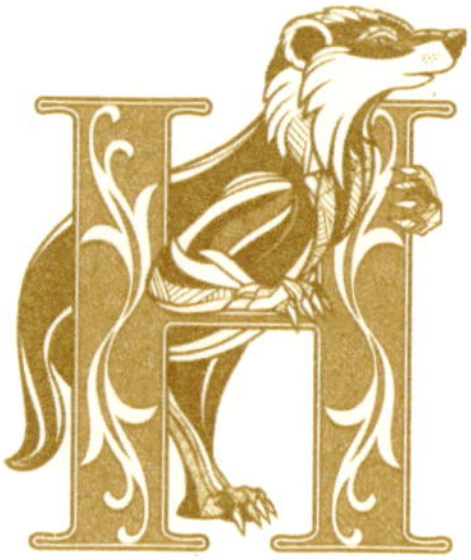

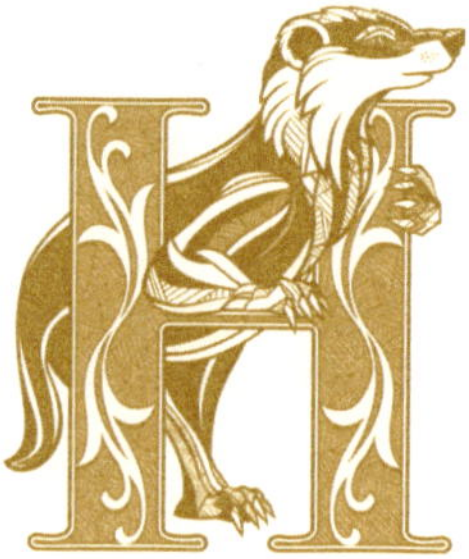

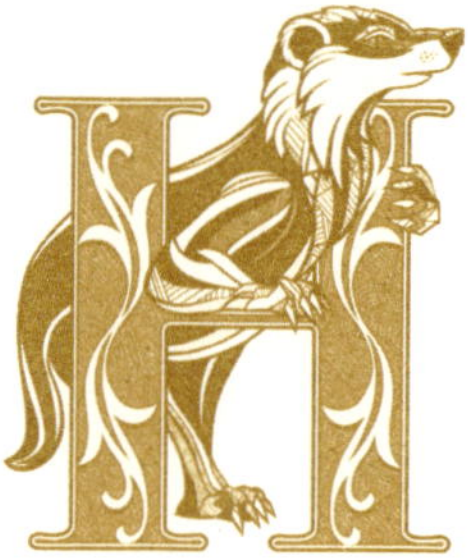

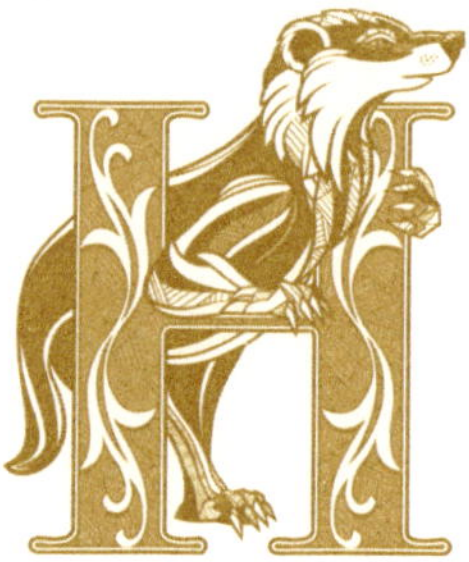

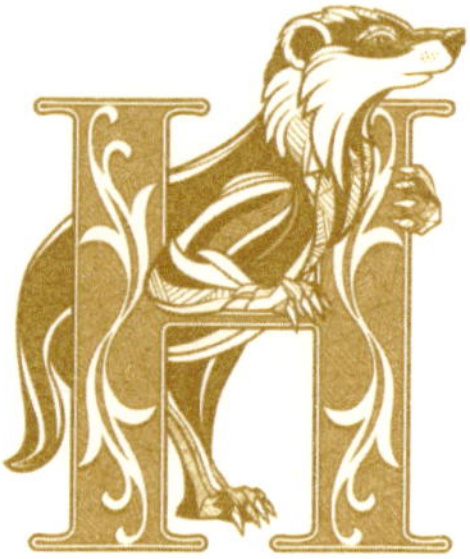

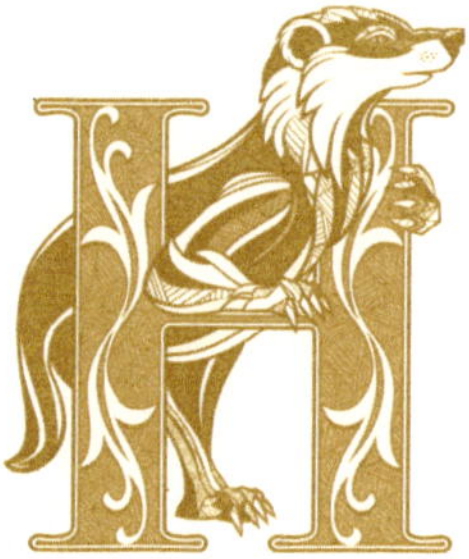

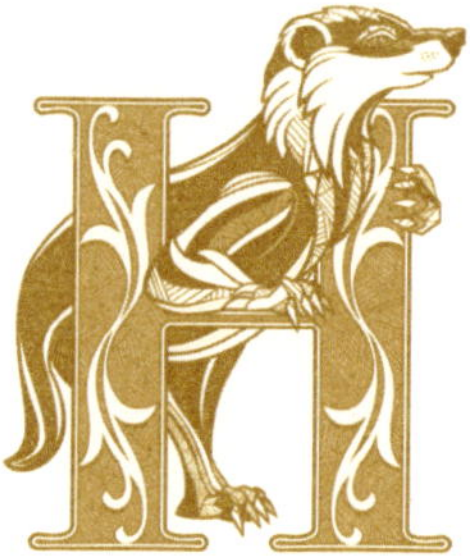

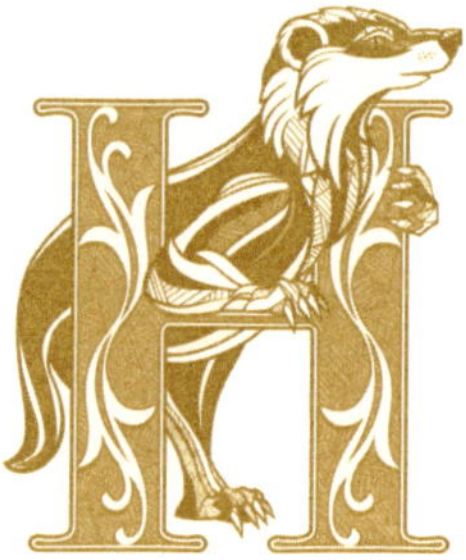

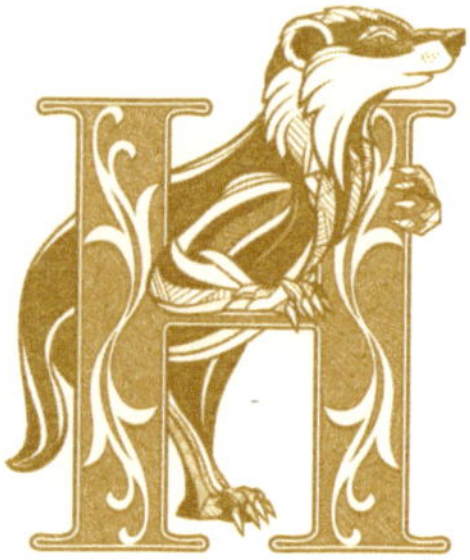

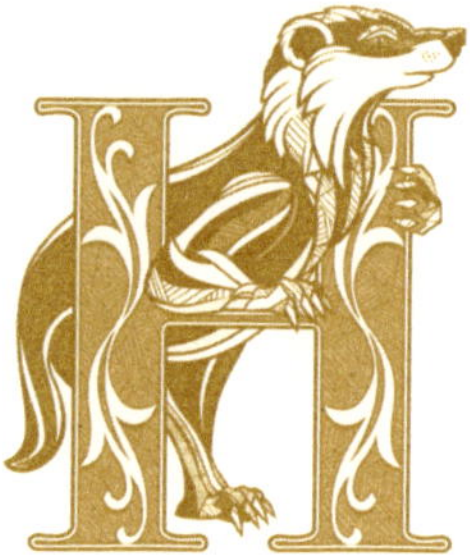

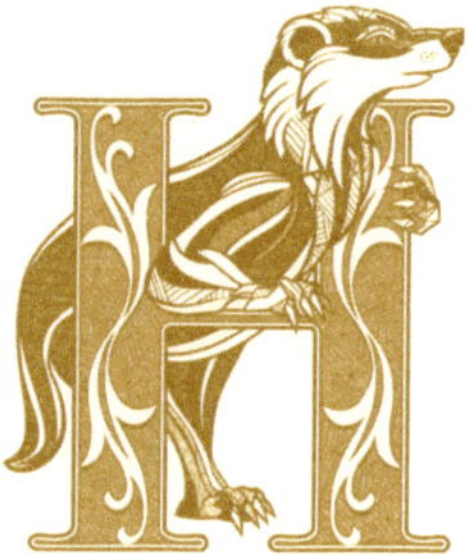

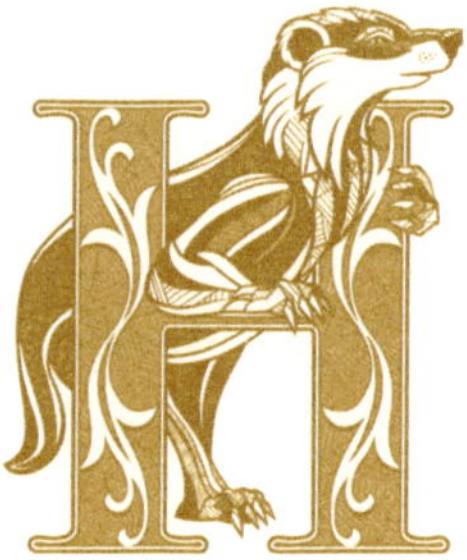

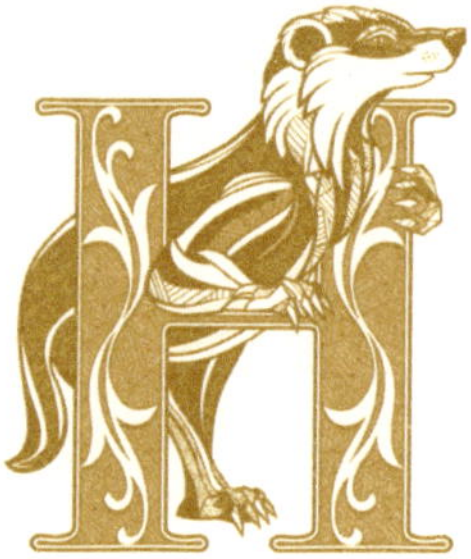

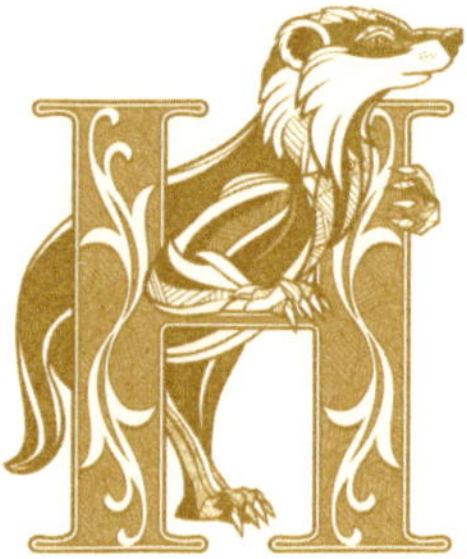

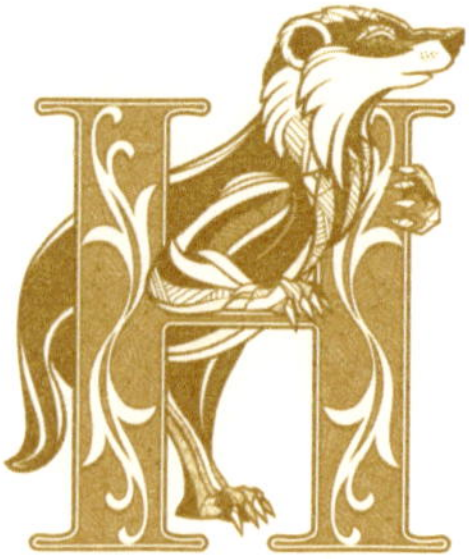

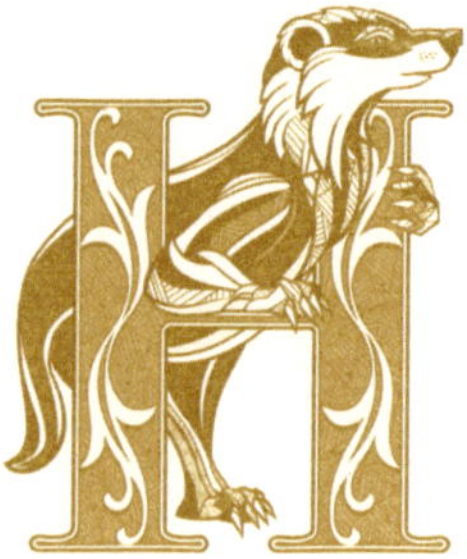

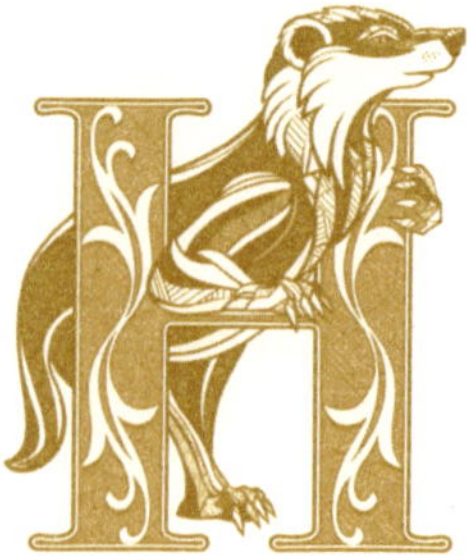

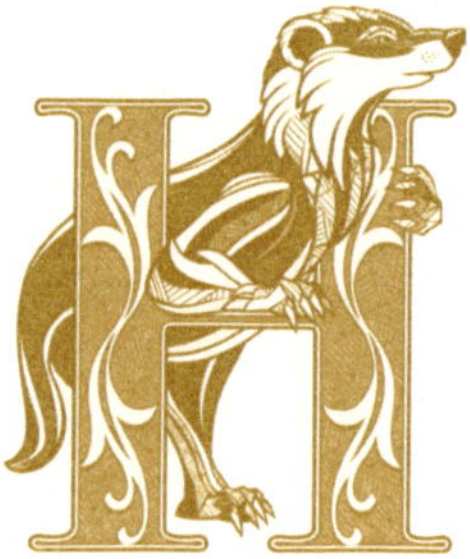

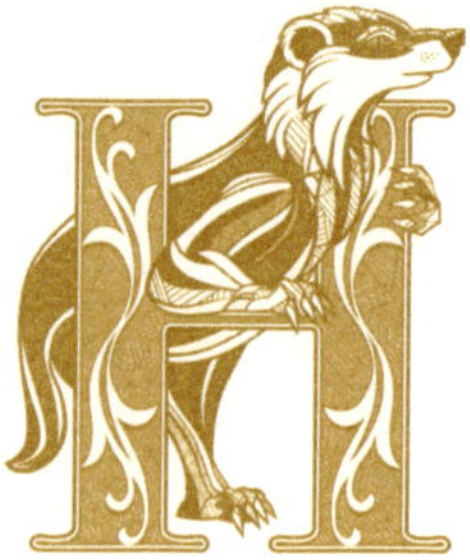

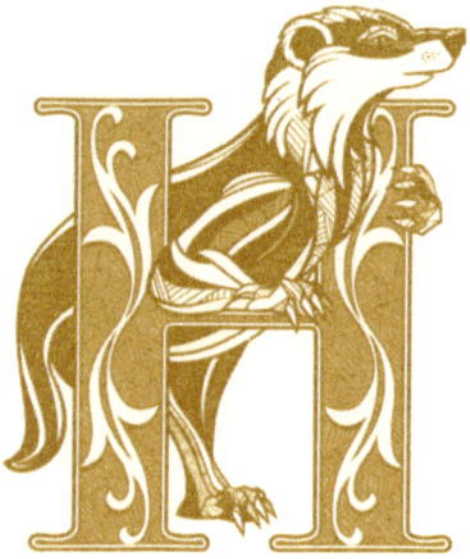

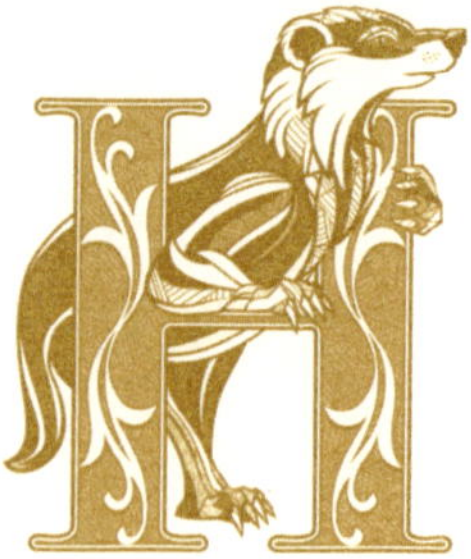

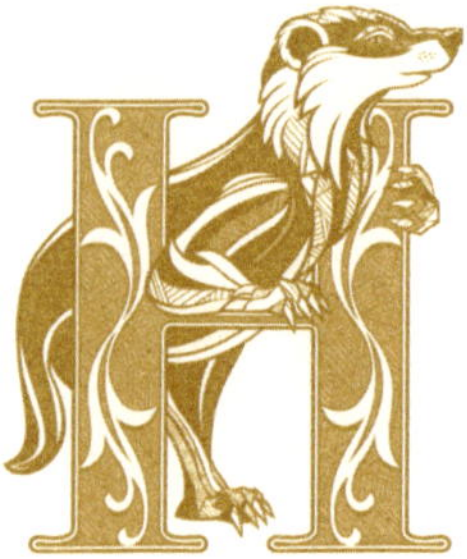

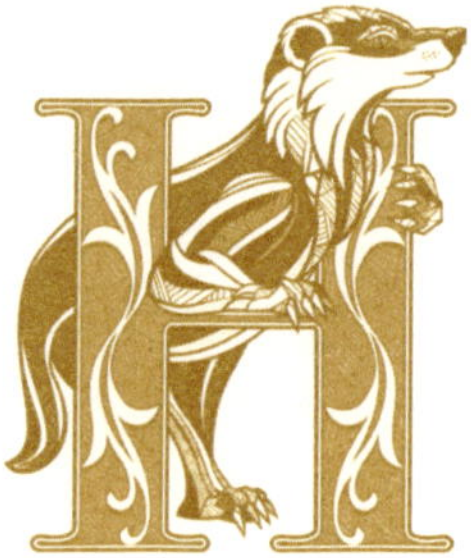

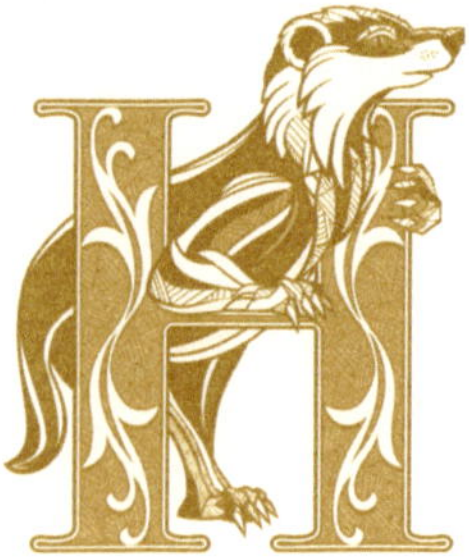

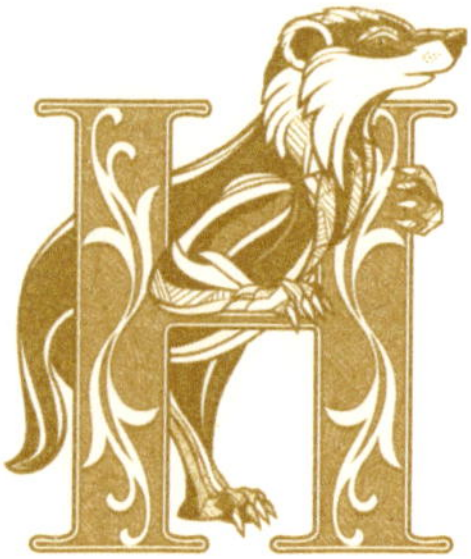

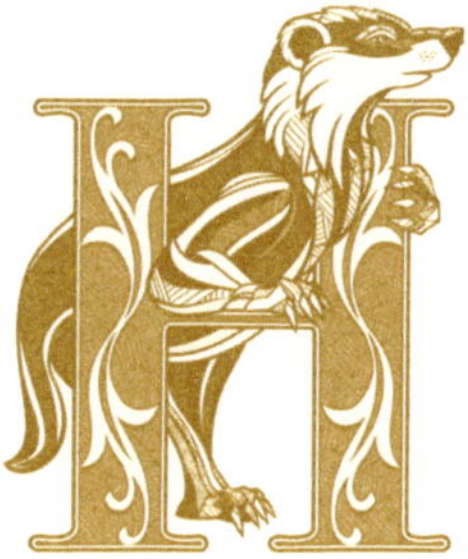

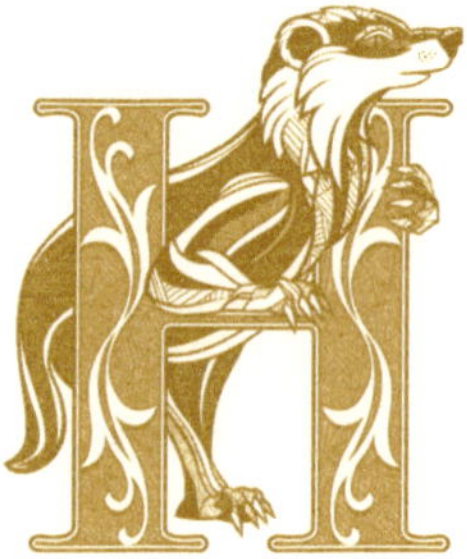

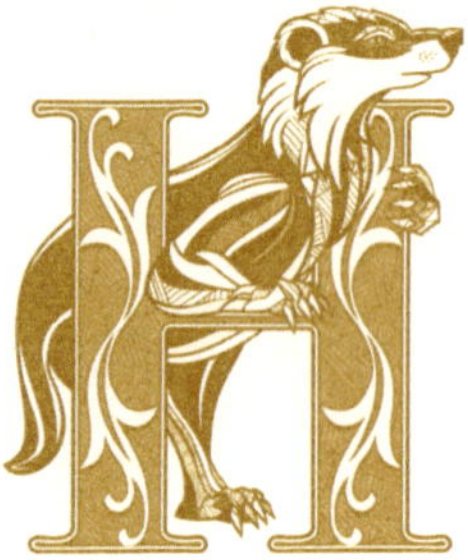

INSIGHT
EDITIONS
insighteditions.com

MANUFACTURED IN CHINA
10 9 8 7 6 5 4 3 2 1